WOODMOUSE LANE

A Nature Story by David Stephen
Illustrated by Marjorie Blamey

D0318329

COLLINS COLOUR CUBS

Woodmouse Lane
was a quiet,
sheltered place,
hedged with haw-
thorn, black-
thorn, dog-rose
and hazel.

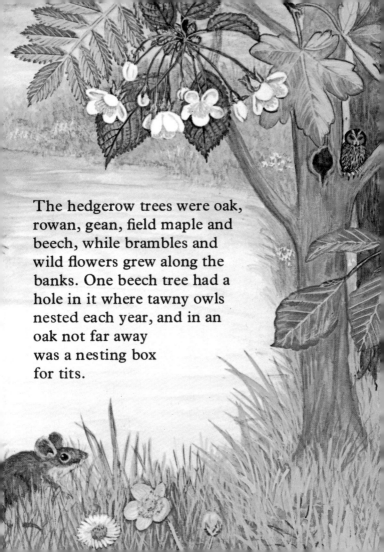

The hedgerow trees were oak, rowan, gean, field maple and beech, while brambles and wild flowers grew along the banks. One beech tree had a hole in it where tawny owls nested each year, and in an oak not far away was a nesting box for tits.

The lane led from Cock Robin's Garden at one end to Frog's Pond at the other, with Squirrel Wood on one side. Woodmouse and his family lived in a part of the lane between the owls' beech tree and the oak with the tit box, and you might say this was their address. They had a lot of woodmice neighbours who lived at other addresses along the lane, and mostly they all stayed at home on their own private property, or *Territory*. But now and again a woodmouse from another address would trespass on Woodmouse's territory and he would chase it away.

Woodmouse came out only at night, so he was a *Nocturnal* animal. He had large, dark eyes which shone when light fell on them, as the eyes of cats and foxes do. He didn't like sunshine, and even when the sun was setting he avoided its light, staying in the shadows until darkness fell. So, if you ever see a woodmouse going about in daylight, you can be sure it's a sick one that doesn't know what it's doing.

Even bright moonlight upset him, and on moonlit nights he would sit just inside his burrow until it was in shadow. On such nights the tawny owls were out and about long before Wood-mouse stirred from home, and he could hear them hooting at roost, and whooping when they were hunting.

Of course,
Woodmouse
couldn't stay
at home just
because the moon
was shining. He had still to go
out in search of food. But he was
always careful to avoid being caught
in the open. And when he
had to cross the lane in
moonlight he scurried as
fast as he was able from
shadow to shadow.

Woodmouse was a digger of burrows, and had his sleeping nest more than two feet below ground in the bank under the hedge. The nest was made of dried grass, which Woodmouse carried home, and shredded finely with his teeth. A tunnel led from his sleeping nest into other tunnels in the bank.

Not far away his mate had her young in a similar nest, deep under the hedge. When they were naked, and very tiny, she spent all day and much of the night with them. But, as they grew stronger, she left them for longer and longer periods and spent more of her time with Woodmouse.

In spring and summer Woodmouse
ate mostly green leafage, and
some buds, but he also caught
and ate a great many insects
and their larvae. On some
nights he hunted most of
the time, catching a
great variety of prey,
and eating hardly any
green food at all.
He liked snails,
which he treated
like hazel nuts,
gnawing through
the shell to
reach the soft
body inside.

For the first fortnight of their lives the baby woodmice lived on their mother's milk. After that they began to follow her from the nest, and make short forays in her company, nibbling at green plants and tender buds, but also pouncing on insects which they ate with squeaks of delight. At three weeks they were weaned, but they remained members of the family and lived at the same address. They played a lot with each other, leaping about like sparks from a fire, and chasing up and down twigs and stems under the hedge.

The tawny owls now had hungry
owlets in the hole in the beech
tree, and each night the cock
bird hunted along the lane for voles
and mice. Woodmouse always froze in
his tracks when the owl appeared and
so escaped his notice. But the owl
killed many woodmice, especially
young ones not as alert as their
parents, and old ones alerted too
late and too slow to move.

Every other night a bitch weasel came to hunt for her kits, which were in a nest under a big stone on the edge of Squirrel Wood. She could catch mice above ground or below, because she was small enough to follow them into the burrow.

The hedgehog was another hunter who came snuffling along after dusk, ready to make a meal of anything he could catch and hold. But he was slow, and a bit clumsy, besides being noisy, so he was really no match for the sprightly wood-mice. When he did catch one it was usually very young, or injured, or already dying of old age. Unlike the weasel he couldn't enter the burrows or dig out the nests.

The fox was different. He would listen
for mouse movement, then stalk towards
it, pinpointing the spot with his nose.
And he was fast and clever. Once he had
fixed the spot where a mouse was nibbling
or sitting he would leap up, forward, and
down, pouncing on it and pinning it down
with his forepaws. He also dug out nests
of young mice. But he rarely wasted time
digging after adults who could escape
along the tunnels.

The badger was another hunter who liked mice. Sometimes he caught them above ground with a lightning snap of his jaws, but mostly he dug out nests of young ones. He had strong claws, like the claws of a bear, and he was a faster and more expert digger than the fox. He was also expert at digging out baby rabbits in their nests.

One night Woodmouse came to the mouth of his burrow to find a badger's face only inches away. The badger snapped at him, but Woodmouse managed to whisk about into the safety of his burrow.

The badger didn't try to dig after him, because he knew that Woodmouse would be far out of reach. And he was. Like the fox, the badger knew enough about wood-mice and their burrows not to waste time digging after them. But Woodmouse got such a scare that he spent more than two hours in hiding, before daring to peep out again.

Later in the summer the little bitch
weasel brought her family to the lane.
The young females were now almost the
size of their mother, and the young
males were bigger. The family padded
around and into the burrows, fairly
stirring up the mice. One of the kits
caught Woodmouse's mate by her tail,
but he couldn't hold her and was left
with only a piece of furred skin in
his jaws.

Although she was badly frightened she wasn't seriously hurt. Woodmice often lose skin off their tails when roughly handled by people, so parting with a bit to a young weasel wasn't such an unusual event. Woodmouse's mate stayed in her nest for a whole day before she felt well enough to go out again.

The skinned part of her tail dried up and withered off, leaving her with a much shorter one which she would have for the rest of her life.

Woodmouse was now meeting many young
mice in the lane at night—hopping
about, climbing up and down the stalks
of plants, or standing tall on their
hindlegs to reach a tender leaf or juicy
insect. They were nearly all from the
same address, or next door, so he seldom
chased any of them. The mice would
feed for an hour or two, then go home
to bed, and come out in the morning dark
to feed again. Woodmouse saw little of
his mate for several nights, because she
had a new family in a new nest not far
from the old one.

On some nights nearly every mouse in
the lane skipped into the cornfield
to nibble at the tender oat blades.
Rabbits nibbled there too, eating much
more than the mice. The thick cover
hid them from the owl, who was hunting
more open ground.

Another place that attracted the mice was Cock Robin's garden, but it was some distance from Woodmouse's home and he didn't go there very often. The younger mice, and the females, didn't go at all, preferring to stay at home. When Woodmouse did make the journey it was always in search of some special tit-bit, like newly planted peas, or young strawberries, or the sweet shoots of flowering plants. When there were many mice in the garden they did a lot of damage to plants. Sometimes the house cat would lie in wait for them, and when he caught a mouse he would play about with it, scaring off the other mice for the rest of the night.

Then there was the tawny owl, who was there every night, either sitting in a tree clicking his beak, or swooping down to catch an unwary mouse or vole. On one of Woodmouse's visits the owl swooped at him, but the bird hit the pea-netting with the tip of one of his wings, which knocked him off balance, and Woodmouse escaped into the potato patch.

Woodmouse knew almost
nothing of what was
happening in the lane by day.

He didn't know that the
blue tits had nine chicks
in the nesting box in the
oak tree, almost over his
head. Nor did he know
about the magpies, nesting
high up in the owl's beech
tree.

Nor did he know about the wasp's nest, about six feet from the ground, in a nearby blackthorn. It was a paper nest, made from wood scrapings which the wasps chewed into pulp, and had been started by the queen wasp herself some weeks before. Since then it had grown from the size of a pigeon's egg to the size of an apple, and it would grow all summer until it was as big as a melon. The wasps were always asleep when Woodmouse woke up, and the blackthorn was one tree he hadn't yet climbed, so he had no experience of wasps going about their everyday habits.

But he knew about the willow warblers,
who had a domed nest lined with feathers
in a bramble thicket, because the
nestlings hissed at him when he poked
his nose into the entrance hole at dusk.
On another night, when he was climbing
down a bramble creeper, the parent birds
called *hoo-eet* and swooped at him. But
once the young willow warblers were
fluttering about on the bramble
creepers the old birds paid no
attention to him.

The bank voles, who lived among the
brambles, were out and about by day as
well as by night, but Woodmouse saw them
only after dark. They weren't hunters
like Woodmouse, and ate almost nothing
but plants and seeds. But they could
be bad-tempered, and Woodmouse was
always wary about going near one when it
was feeding, because it would squeak
and show its teeth at him, and even
threaten to attack him.

The fox often hunted bank voles, but he had to wait until one scurried clear of the brambles, because he didn't like having his face cut by the prickly creepers. Having to wait didn't upset him if he really wanted vole. So he thought nothing of crouching for ten or fifteen minutes until a vole was far enough from the brambles to be caught in the open.

Although the fox was far too wise to waste his time digging after adult woodmice in their tunnels, there was a morning when he did waste his time, after he had narrowly missed catching Woodmouse in the open. Maybe it was because he was angry at missing, or because he had nothing better to do. Anyway he did dig, and Woodmouse, safe in his nest, could hear the thud of his paws.

As the summer wore on Woodmouse ate
more and more green food and fewer
insects, but he was always ready to
pounce on a caterpillar or a centipede.
One thing he could never resist,
no matter what else he was eating,
was a snail, and like all woodmice he
had his special way of opening it.
He gnawed through the hard shell,
away from the spiral, making the
same kind of hole as he did in a
hazel nut, and leaving his tiny
tooth marks round the edge. Other
hunters eat snails, of course.
The thrush and the hedgehog are two.
But they break them. Crows and other
birds do the same.
Only the woodmouse
treats a snail like
a hazel nut.

The lane is now a busy place. Woodmouse's mate has her new family out of
the nest. Young shrews scurry about,
wrinkling their long snouts, seeking
prey in the leaf litter. A baby rabbit
nibbles a corn stalk under the hedge.

The young tawny owls, strong on the wing and fit to hunt on their own, broke up many such happy gatherings. They, too, had to eat. The lane was their home ground, and mice, voles and shrews were their prey. So they hunted a lot in the lane. When one of them swooped, the mice and others scattered, but more often than not the owl would fly up with a mouse, or vole, or shrew, clutched in a foot. There were nights when Woodmouse was the chosen prey, but he always managed to be that bit quicker than the owl.

A carrion crow came to roost
at night in the oak tree, and
he could hear the voles and
mice moving about under the
hedge. His eyes were sharp
enough to spot a young woodmouse coming out too early,
and he was smart
enough to swoop
down and catch it.

Woodmouse knew about the
crow because he could hear
him chuckling to himself
on his perch after dark,
but he had no idea what a
crow looked like. He knew
vaguely about the sparrow-
hawk, for he had seen her
flapping across the lane,
from one tree to another, when she was
restless at roost. What he didn't know
was that she hunted and killed small
birds in the lane during the day, when
he was in his nest asleep.

One hunter he did know was the farm cat, which sat for two hours one night outside his burrow, waiting for him to appear.

But Woodmouse stayed in his nest until the cat lost patience and went away.

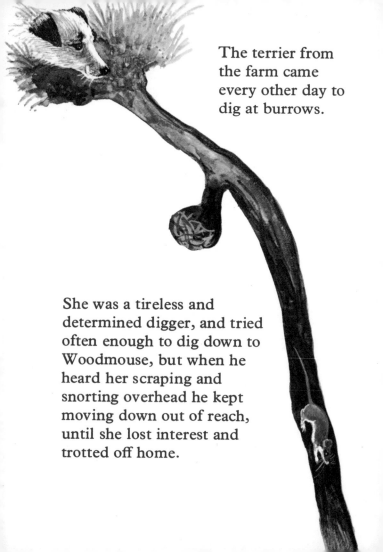

The terrier from the farm came every other day to dig at burrows.

She was a tireless and determined digger, and tried often enough to dig down to Woodmouse, but when he heard her scraping and snorting overhead he kept moving down out of reach, until she lost interest and trotted off home.

By early autumn
Woodmouse had
become fat and
sleek.

The badger from Squirrel Wood had also
put on fat, and was eating as much as
he could to grow still fatter. There
would be stormy nights in the winter
ahead when he would stay in bed, with
nothing to eat, and the extra fat
would keep him going. One night he
reared against the blackthorn, and
shook it until the wasp's nest fell
to the ground. Then he tore it open
with his claws and ate all the grubs.

Well, not quite all of them. Later in
the night Woodmouse found a few he had
missed and ate them. He liked them,
but with wild berries now so plentiful
Woodmouse became more and more a fruit
eater and less and less a hunter, even
ignoring an insect right in front of
his nose if he was nibbling at a juicy
bramble. The younger mice still hunted
a lot, far more so than the adults,
but every mouse and vole in the lane
gathered its full share of the berry
harvest.

Of course, there were far more berries in the lane than the mice could ever eat, but they wouldn't be there all winter. Before long the birds would be eating them too, and they would quickly disappear. So the woodmice, instead of eating then going to bed, began to gather the berries and store them. Woodmouse filled a yellow-hammer's old nest with haws and covered his store over with withered grass.

He found an old milk bottle under the
hedge and stored haws and ears of corn
in it; then he packed the neck of the
bottle with soil and twigs and went to
bed. When he came out at dusk he was
hungry, and for the rest of the night
he was so busy eating and sleeping that
he had no time to carry food for storing.
He began to use the old nest of a black-
bird as an eating place, climbing out
to collect a haw or a doghip, or down
to the ground for an acorn, then carry-
ing it to the nest to nibble
it. He ate the tips of dog-
hips, leaving the glossy,
red skins in the
nest or letting
them fall to the
ground.

Although he hid food in a number of
places he carried a lot underground
and stored it near his nest, or even
in it. He carried in acorns, hazel
nuts, rowans, corn, a piece of bark,
some dead leaves and six wild
hyacinth bulbs. When he ate corn on
his doorstep he left coarse nibblings
to betray his presence; and when he
left an empty hazel shell there it
betrayed him by his special mark.

Later in the autumn he found wasp
grubs scattered beside a hole that
had been the entrance to a woodmouse burrow. Wasps had taken it
over, and enlarged it throughout the
summer, and now it contained a paper
nest as big as a football. But the
great fortress of a thousand stings
was empty. The workers had left
to die; the young queens to seek a
place in which to sleep through the
winter. Wood-
mouse entered
warily to
explore.

The wasp's nest had seven storeys, with pillars of paper between them. Woodmouse had to gnaw his way into the heart of the nest, tossing aside dead wasps, and cells containing dead grubs. He liked the place and began to carry nuts, acorns and berries into it. Then he had another thought and brought in withered grass, which he chewed and shredded with his teeth. He nibbled out the heart of the wasps' nest, then mixed his shredded grass with the bits of paper to make a wood-mouse nest. So now he had a woodmouse nest, inside a wasps' nest, which had been built by a queen wasp inside what had been a woodmouse hole in the first place!

Although he had more food stored than he was ever likely to need during the winter, he didn't begin to use it at once. He fed on what still remained in the hedgerows, using an old bird nest as a platform, and the ground below soon became littered with the shells of haws, hips and nuts.

When the first frosts came he often used
his nest-within-a-nest to sleep in, and
when he woke up he had a store of food
beside him. He could eat at any time
he liked during the day or night. On
other days he used his other sleeping
nest, where he also had a store of food.
Then there were the other stores he had
laid up—in the yellowhammer's nest,
in the milk bottle, and underground.
These stores he shared with other mice,
but the stores in his two nests he used
only himself.

Woodmouse was now well provided for. He was fit and fat and sleek, and seemingly in the best of health. But he was now an old mouse by mouse-time, and few wood-mice live through a second winter. I can't tell you how he fared that winter, and in a way I'm glad I can't.

ISBN 0 00 123284 3
Text copyright © 1978 David Stephen
Illustrations copyright © 1978 Marjorie Blamey
Printed and made in Great Britain